SING-ALONG
Swing
WITH A LIVE BAND!

WISE PUBLICATIONS
part of The Music Sales Group
London / New York / Paris / Sydney / Copenhagen / Berlin / Madrid / Hong Kong / Tokyo

Published by
Wise Publications
14-15 Berners Street, London W1T 3LJ, UK.

Exclusive Distributors:
Music Sales Limited
Distribution Centre, Newmarket Road, Bury St Edmunds, Suffolk IP33 3YB, UK.
Music Sales Pty Limited
20 Resolution Drive, Caringbah, NSW 2229, Australia.

Order No. AM999031
ISBN 978-1-84938-311-0
This book © Copyright 2010 Wise Publications,
a division of Music Sales Limited.

Compiled by Nick Crispin
Edited by Lizzie Moore
Music arranged by Paul Honey
Music processed by Paul Ewers Music Design
Song Background Notes by Michael Heatley
Cover design by Fresh Lemon & Adela Casacuberta
Cover illustration by Adela Casacuberta
Text photographs courtesy LFI
Printed in the EU

CD recorded, mixed and mastered by Jonas Persson
Vocals: Ruth Searle and Jeff Shadley
Instrumental solos: Howard McGill
Keyboard: Paul Honey
Bass: Allen Walley
Drums: Chris Baron

Your Guarantee of Quality
As publishers, we strive to produce every book to the highest
commercial standards. This book has been carefully designed
to minimise awkward page turns and to make playing from it
a real pleasure. Particular care has been given to specifying
acid-free, neutral-sized paper made from pulps which have
not been elemental chlorine bleached. This pulp is from farmed
sustainable forests and was produced with special regard for
the environment. Throughout, the printing and binding have
been planned to ensure a sturdy, attractive publication which
should give years of enjoyment. If your copy fails to meet our
high standards, please inform us and we will gladly replace it.

www.musicsales.com

FREE bonus material.

Visit www.hybridpublications.com

Registration is free and easy.

Your registration code is: VV110

Song Background Notes

April In Paris
Count Basie

Count Basie, who died in 1984 aged 79, led a big band for nearly half a century and ranked alongside Duke Ellington as the most popular jazzman on the world stage. The lyrical 'April In Paris' was composed in 1932 by Vernon Duke with words by E. Y. 'Yip' Harburg for the Broadway musical *Walk A Little Faster*, but Basie's definitive 1955 interpretation (featuring trumpeter Thad Jones' famous 'Pop Goes The Weasel' solo) won a deserved place in the Grammy Hall of Fame.

Crazy Rhythm
Chet Baker

Although Oklahoma-born trumpeter Chet Baker died in 1988, his music found a fresh audience as a new millennium began thanks to extensive use of his music in the Oscar-nominated movie *The Talented Mr Ripley*. The number 'Crazy Rhythm' first surfaced in 1928 when it was written by Irving Caesar, Joseph Meyer and Roger Wolfe Kahn for the Broadway musical *Here's Howe*. The swinging 32-bar showtune, first recorded by Roger Wolfe Kahn's Orchestra, has since become a jazz standard thanks to Baker and others.

Flying Home
Lionel Hampton

Multi-instrumentalist Lionel Hampton fronted a band longer than any other swing-era legend. Wife Gladys encouraged him to concentrate on the vibraphone, considered a novelty instrument at that time, and with it he created an amalgam of swinging jazz and driving rhythm and blues. 'Flying Home' was his signature tune, composed on his first aeroplane trip in 1939 as he and fellow members of Benny Goodman's band flew from Los Angeles to a gig in Atlantic City on the east coast.

Honeysuckle Rose
Fats Waller

Thomas 'Fats' Waller graduated from accompanying blues legend Bessie Smith, as a teenager, to signing with Victor Records in 1934. By this time the ebullient pianist had formed a partnership with lyricist Andy Razaf, with whom he composed many of his famous tunes including 'Ain't Misbehavin' and this song, 'Honeysuckle Rose'. Introduced as a dance number in the 1929 revue *Load Of Coal* at Connie's Inn in Harlem, it was to be one of his first recordings and was inducted in the Grammy Hall of Fame in 1999.

I've Heard That Song Before
Harry James

One of the finest of all big-band trumpet players, with fine articulation and a genuine ability to stir the audience, trumpeter Harry James was encouraged by Benny Goodman to form his own outfit. The hits followed, including 1942's 'I've Heard That Song Before', penned by Jule Styne and Sammy Cahn. Frank Sinatra covered the song, cementing its status as a swing classic, while James' version of the song, with vocals contributed by Helen Forrest, can be heard in Woody Allen's movie *Hannah And Her Sisters*.

Perdido
Juan Tizol / Duke Ellington

The impact of Edward Kennedy 'Duke' Ellington on the jazz scene spread over six decades as musician, arranger and bandleader, his work reaching beyond the confines of a minority-appeal music. Trombonist Juan Tizol wrote only two tunes with his boss during a 15-year stint with Ellington's band from 1929 but both 'Caravan' and the featured 'Perdido' have become standards, the latter meaning 'lost' in Spanish.

Satin Doll
Duke Ellington / Billy Strayhorn

Duke Ellington's golden era from the late '20s to the mid '40s in which he made his name as both a writer and bandleader, was given a further dimension with the recruitment of pianist/arranger Billy Strayhorn in 1939. The lyrics to 'Satin Doll' were written by Johnny Mercer after the song was already a hit in its instrumental form, Ellington having used it as the closing number at most of his concerts, and it has since been recorded by such illustrious artists as Ella Fitzgerald and Frank Sinatra.

Stardust
Hoagy Carmichael / Artie Shaw

Born in 1899, Hoagland Howard 'Hoagy' Carmichael wrote numbers for artists such as Louis Armstrong and Bing Crosby to perform in movies, but later took cameo roles in films singing the songs he created. Carmichael's classic was 1929's 'Stardust', which he wrote two years earlier; Mitchell Parish added words in May that year, a student having named it because, "It sounded like dust from stars drifting down through the summer sky". Clarinettist Artie Shaw's recording of the tune sold many millions of 78rpm records.

'Tain't What You Do (It's The Way That Cha Do It)
Sy Oliver / Jimmie Lunceford

The combination of bandleader Jimmie Lunceford and arranger Sy Oliver resulted in some memorable music created in just a few late-'30s years. "Tain't What You Do...' was just one of the swing classics they wrote together, exhibiting Oliver's trademarks of, "Two-beat rhythm, stop-time breaks, intricate saxophone choruses and ear-splitting brass explosions". Oliver defected to Tommy Dorsey in 1939, but "Tain't What You Do...' lived on in the hands of Ella Fitzgerald, the Fun Boy Three and many others.

Tuxedo Junction
Erskine Hawkins / Glenn Miller

Though his aeroplane went down in mysterious circumstances in 1944, Glenn Miller's musical legacy continues to fly high today. His trademark sound was the combination of clarinet and four saxes plus the repeated riff that fades away before reappearing. Erskine Hawkins, who wrote 'Tuxedo Junction' was a prominent African-American trumpeter, bandleader and Miller contemporary during the big-band era. He named the number after an area of Birmingham, Alabama.

Glenn Miller

Duke Ellington

Chet Baker

Harry James

Count Basie

Fats Waller

April In Paris

Words & Music by Vernon Duke & E. Y. Harburg

Demo track: Track 01
Backing track: Track 11

Moderate swing

A-pril in Par - is,_____ ches-nuts in blos - som._____

Hol - i - day ta - bles_____ un - der the trees._____ A-pril in Par - is,_____

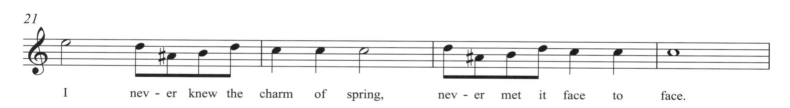

this is a feel - ing_____ no-one can ev - er_____ re - prise.

I nev - er knew the charm of spring, nev - er met it face to face.

I nev - er knew my heart could sing, nev - er missed a warm em - brace, till,

A - pril in Par - is._____ Whom can I run to?_____

What have you done to_____ my heart?_____

Crazy Rhythm

Words by Irving Caesar
Music by Joseph Meyer & Roger Wolfe Kahn

Demo track: Track 02
Backing track: Track 12

Bright swing

Cra - zy rhy - thm here's the door - way, I'll go my way

you'll go your__ way. Cra - zy rhy - thm from now on__ we're through.

Here is where we have a show - down, I'm too high - brow, your too low__ down.

Cra - zy rhy - thm here's good - bye__ to you. They say that

when a high - brow meets a low - brow walk - ing a - long broad - way.

Soon the high - brow, he has no__ brow. Ain't it a shame,__ and who's to blame?

What's the use of pro - hi - bi - tion? You pro - duce the same con - di - tion.

Cra - zy rhy - thm I've gone cra - zy too.

Cra - zy rhy - thm here's the door - way, I'll go my way you go your__ way.

Cra - zy rhy - thm from now on__ we're through.

Here is where we have a show - down. I'm too high - brow, you're too low__ down.

Cra - zy rhy - thm here's good - bye__ to you. They say that

when a high - brow meets a low - brow walk - ing a - long broad - way.

Soon the high - brow, he has no__ brow. Ain't it a shame, and who's to blame?

What's the use of pro - hi - bi - tion? You pro - duce the same con - di - tion.

Cra - zy rhy - thm, I've gone cra - zy too.

Flying Home

Music by Benny Goodman & Lionel Hampton

Demo track: Track 03
Backing track: Track 13

Bright swing

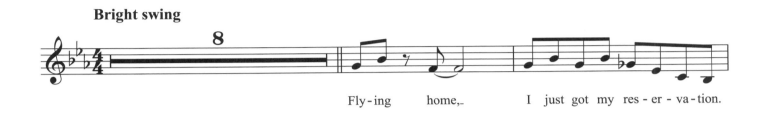

Fly - ing home,— I just got my res - er - va - tion.

Fly - ing home,— cur - tain's straight a - cross the na - tion. Fly - ing home,—

won't you meet me at the sta - tion, got - ta be with you.— Fly - ing home,—

sprout - ing wings up - on my back. I'm fly - ing home,— I am on the fast - er track. I'm

fly - ing home,— ba - by, won't you take me back, I got - ta be with you.—

Ev - er since I_____ went a - way,_____ I've been_____ feel - ing blue._____

Pack - ing up my clothes to - day_____ fly - ing_____ home to you._____

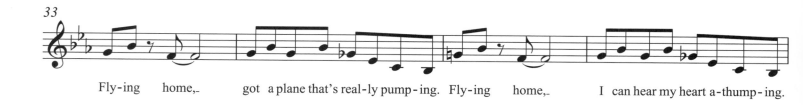

Fly - ing home,_ got a plane that's real - ly pump - ing. Fly - ing home,_ I can hear my heart a - thump - ing.

Fly - ing home,_ gee I want to tell you some - thing, got - ta be with you._____

Trumpet solo

E♭7

15

Ev - er since I_____ went a - way,_____ I've been_____ feel - ing blue._____

Pack - ing up my clothes to - day_____ fly - ing_____ home to you._____

Honeysuckle Rose

Words by Andy Razaf
Music by Fats Waller

Demo track: Track 04
Backing track: Track 14

Medium swing

69 Ev-'ry hon-ey bee___ fills with jeal-ou-sy, when they see you out with me. I don't blame them

73 good-ness knows.___ When you're pass-in' by,___ flow-ers droop and sigh___

79 and I know the reas-on why. You're much sweet-er, good-ness knows.___

85 Don't buy su - gar,___ you___ just___ have to touch my cup.___

89 You're my su - gar,___ it's sweet___ when you stir it up.___

93 Ev -'ry hon - ey bee fills with jeal - ous - y, when they see you out with

96 me. I don't blame them good - ness knows, I don't blame them good - ness knows,

rall.

100 I don't blame them good - ness knows, hon - ey - suck - le rose.

Perdido

Words by Ervin Drake & Harry Lenk
Music by Juan Tizol

Demo track: Track 05
Backing track: Track 15

I've Heard That Song Before

Words by Sammy Cahn
Music by Jule Styne

Demo track: Track 06
Backing track: Track 16

seems_____ to me I've heard that song__ be - fore____ its from an old fa - mil - iar score.

____ I know it well, that mel - o - dy._____

It's fun - ny how it feels,__ re - calls a fav - our - ite dream._

A dream that brought you so close__ to me. I know each

word___ be - cause I've heard that song__ be - fore____ the ly - rics said for - ev - er - more,__ for - ev - er-

- more so mem - or - y._____ Please have them play it a - gain,__

and I re - mem - ber just when,__ I heard that love - ly song be -

- fore,_____ I heard that love - ly song be - fore,_____ I

heard that love - ly song be - fore.

Satin Doll

Words by Johnny Mercer
Music by Duke Ellington & Billy Strayhorn

Demo track: Track 07
Backing track: Track 17

23

And that 'n' my sat - in doll.____

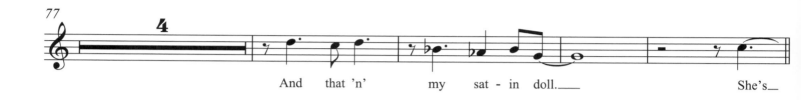

And that 'n' my sat - in doll.____ She's____

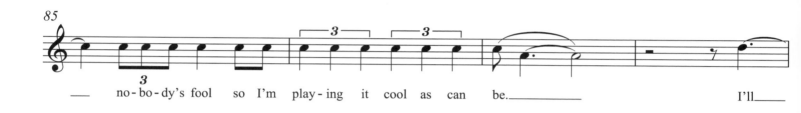

____ no - bo - dy's fool so I'm play - ing it cool as can be._____ I'll____

____ give it a whirl but I ain't for no girl catch - in' me. Switch - e - roo - ney.____

Te - le - phone num - ber, well__ you know I'm do - in' my__rhum - ba, with u - no,

And that 'n' my sat - in doll.____

And that 'n' my sat - in doll.____

'Tain't What You Do

(It's The Way That Cha Do It)

Words & Music by Sy Oliver & James Young

Demo track: Track 08
Backing track: Track 18

35 what you do it's the place that you do it, 'tain't what you do it's the time that you do it, 'tain't

39 what you do it's the way that you do it. That's what gets re - sults.___

Saxophone solo

43 G G⁷/B C D⁷ G G⁷/B C D⁷

47 G G⁷/B C C#dim⁷ G/D

51 G G⁷/B C D⁷ G G⁷/B C D⁷

55 G G⁷/B C C#dim⁷ G/D

59 'Tain't what you do it's the way that you do it, 'tain't what you do it's the way that you do it, 'tain't

63 what you do it's the way that you do it. That's what gets re - sults. sults. 'Tain't

Stardust

Words by Mitchell Parish
Music by Hoagy Carmichael

Demo track: Track 09
Backing track: Track 19

Medium ballad Straight ♪s

And now the pur - ple dusk of twi - light time, steals a - cross the mead - ows of my

heart. High up in the sky the lit - tle stars climb, Al - ways re - mind - ing me that we're a - part.

You won - der down the lane and far a - way, leav - ing me a song that will not die.

Swing feel

Love is now the star dust of yes - ter - day, the mu - sic of the years gone by. Some - times I

won - der why I spend the lone - ly night___ dream - ing of a song. The

mel - o - dy,___ haunts my rev - e - rie and I am once a - gain with you.___ When our

love was new   and each kiss an in-spi-ra - tion.   But

that was long a-go   and now my con-so-la-tion is   in the star-dust of a song.   Be -

-side a gar-den wall   when stars are bright___   you are in my arms.   The

night-in-gale_   tells his fai-ry-tale   of par-a-dise where ro-ses grew.___ Though I

dream in vain_____   in my heart it will re - main,   my

star-dust mel-o-dy_____   the mem-o-ry of loves re-frain,   my

rall.

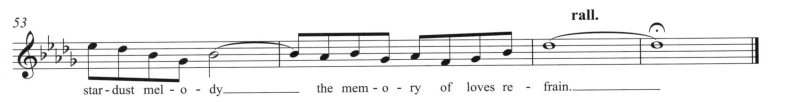

star-dust mel-o-dy_____   the mem-o-ry of loves re-frain._____

Tuxedo Junction

**Words & Music by Buddy Feyne, Erskine Hawkins,
William Johnson & Julian Dash**

Demo track: Track 10
Backing track: Track 20

CD Track Listing

DEMONSTRATION TRACKS

1 **April In Paris** (Duke/Harburg) Carlin Music Corporation/Boosey & Hawkes Music Publishers Limited.

2 **Crazy Rhythm** (Caesar/Meyer/Kahn) Redwood Music Limited/Warner/Chappell North America Limited.

3 **Flying Home** (Goodman/Hampton) Lafleur Music Limited.

4 **Honeysuckle Rose** (Razaf/Waller) Redwood Music Limited/IQ Music Limited.

5 **Perdido** (Drake/Lenk/Tizol) Campbell Connelly & Company Limited.

6 **I've Heard That Song Before** (Cahn/Styne) Warner/Chappell Music Limited.

7 **Satin Doll** (Mercer/Ellington/Strayhorn) Campbell Connelly & Company Limited.

8 **'Tain't What You Do (It's The Way That Cha Do It)** (Oliver/Young) Universal/MCA Music Limited.

9 **Stardust** (Parish/Carmichael) Lawrence Wright Music Company Limited/Peermusic (UK) Limited.

10 **Tuxedo Junction** (Feyne/Hawkins/Johnson/Dash) Lafleur Music Limited.

BACKING TRACKS

11 **April In Paris**

12 **Crazy Rhythm**

13 **Flying Home**

14 **Honeysuckle Rose**

15 **Perdido**

16 **I've Heard That Song Before**

17 **Satin Doll**

18 **'Tain't What You Do (It's The Way That Cha Do It)**

19 **Stardust**

20 **Tuxedo Junction**